TO...

G000043164

I PROMISE...

...TO BRING YOU
BREAKFAST IN BED WITH
A ROSE AND A SMILE.

SIGNED...   DATE.....................

LOVE MAKES THE WORLD GO ROUND...

TO...

I PROMISE...

...TO TRY SOMETHING
NEW AND ADVENTUROUS
WITH YOU, LIKE SAILING
OR CLIMBING.

SIGNED.. DATE.....................

LOVE MAKES THE WORLD GO ROUND...

TO...

I PROMISE...

...TO MAKE YOU A
SPECIAL MEAL WORTHY
OF A MICHELIN STAR.

SIGNED.. DATE...........

LOVE MAKES THE WORLD GO ROUND...

TO...

I PROMISE...

...TO BE SPONTANEOUSLY
ROMANTIC FOR A WEEK.

SIGNED...   DATE.......................

LOVE MAKES THE WORLD GO ROUND...

TO..

...TO BRING YOU A
PICNIC FOR YOUR
LUNCH HOUR.

SIGNED.. DATE......................

LOVE MAKES THE WORLD GO ROUND...

TO..

I PROMISE...

...TO TAKE YOU TO SEE
A ROMANTIC PLAY OR
MUSICAL OF YOUR CHOICE.

SIGNED... DATE.........

LOVE MAKES THE WORLD GO ROUND...

TO...

I PROMISE...

...TO TAKE UP DANCE
CLASSES WITH YOU.

SIGNED.. DATE......................

LOVE MAKES THE WORLD GO ROUND...

TO..

I PROMISE...

...TO TAKE YOU ON A GLAMOROUS DAY OUT TO THE RACES.

SIGNED.. DATE.....................

LOVE MAKES THE WORLD GO ROUND...

TO...

...TO LEARN A LOVE POEM BY HEART AND RECITE IT TO YOU BEFORE BED.

SIGNED... DATE...........

LOVE MAKES THE WORLD GO ROUND...

TO..

 I PROMISE... ...TO IRON THE SHEETS
AND FLUFF UP YOUR
PILLOWS, AND WARM
YOUR SIDE OF THE BED
BEFORE YOU GET IN.

SIGNED.. DATE.....................

LOVE MAKES THE WORLD GO ROUND...

TO...

...TO RUN YOU A
LUXURIOUS CANDLELIT
BUBBLE-BATH, AND
POUR SOME CHAMPAGNE
BUBBLES TOO.

SIGNED..   DATE......................

LOVE MAKES THE WORLD GO ROUND...

TO...

I PROMISE...

...TO WATCH YOUR
FAVOURITE MOVIE
WITH YOU (WITHOUT
COMPLAINING!).

SIGNED.. DATE............

LOVE MAKES THE WORLD GO ROUND...

TO..

I PROMISE...

...TO TAKE YOU OUT TO
A CLUB AND DANCE THE
NIGHT AWAY.

SIGNED..   DATE.......................

LOVE MAKES THE WORLD GO ROUND...

TO...

I PROMISE...

...TO ATTEND THE EVENT
OF YOUR CHOICE
WITH YOU.

SIGNED.. DATE......................

LOVE MAKES THE WORLD GO ROUND...

TO..

I PROMISE...

...TO WRITE YOU A
LOVE LETTER.

SIGNED.. DATE.........

LOVE MAKES THE WORLD GO ROUND...

TO...

I PROMISE...

...TO SERENADE YOU
WITH A ROMANTIC SONG.

SIGNED.. DATE.....................

LOVE MAKES THE WORLD GO ROUND...

TO..

I PROMISE...

...TO TAKE YOU ON A
MYSTERY DAY OUT.

SIGNED.. DATE.....................

LOVE MAKES THE WORLD GO ROUND...

TO...

I PROMISE...

...TO FIND SEVEN NEW
WAYS TO SAY 'I LOVE
YOU' THIS WEEK.

SIGNED.. DATE.................

LOVE MAKES THE WORLD GO ROUND...

TO...

I PROMISE...

...TO SPEND A WHOLE
WEEKEND WITH YOU
ON OUR OWN.

SIGNED.. DATE.........................

LOVE MAKES THE WORLD GO ROUND...

TO...

I PROMISE...

...TO LET YOU LISTEN TO YOUR FAVOURITE MUSIC ALL EVENING.

SIGNED... DATE.........................

LOVE MAKES THE WORLD GO ROUND...

TO..

I PROMISE...

...TO LIE IN ON A SUNDAY AND SNUGGLE UNDER THE DUVET WITH YOU.

SIGNED.. DATE........

LOVE MAKES THE WORLD GO ROUND...

TO..

I PROMISE...

...TO TREAT YOU LIKE
ROYALTY WHILE YOU'RE
POORLY.

SIGNED.. DATE.....................

LOVE MAKES THE WORLD GO ROUND...

TO...

...TO TAKE YOU
SHOPPING TO YOUR
FAVOURITE CLOTHES
STORE AND WAIT
PATIENTLY WHILE YOU
TRY EVERYTHING ON.

SIGNED... DATE...................

LOVE MAKES THE WORLD GO ROUND...

TO...

I PROMISE...

...TO TAKE YOU
ON A ROMANTIC
WEEKEND AWAY.

SIGNED... DATE.........

LOVE MAKES THE WORLD GO ROUND...

TO...

I PROMISE...

...TO MAKE A LIST OF THE TOP TEN REASONS WHY I LOVE YOU AND READ IT ALOUD.

SIGNED.. DATE........................

LOVE MAKES THE WORLD GO ROUND...

TO...

I PROMISE...

...TO DO A SWEET
FAVOUR FOR YOU EVERY
DAY FOR A WEEK.

SIGNED.. DATE.......................

LOVE MAKES THE WORLD GO ROUND...

TO...

I PROMISE...

...TO MAKE THIS
VALENTINE'S DAY
EXTRA SPECIAL.

SIGNED.. DATE...........

LOVE MAKES THE WORLD GO ROUND...

TO...

...TO DECLARE MY LOVE
FOR YOU IN PUBLIC.

SIGNED... DATE.......................

LOVE MAKES THE WORLD GO ROUND...

TO...

I PROMISE...

...TO BRING YOU
FLOWERS EVERY
WEEK FOR A MONTH.

SIGNED..   DATE.....................

LOVE MAKES THE WORLD GO ROUND...

TO...

I PROMISE...

...TO PEEL GRAPES FOR
YOU AND FEED THEM TO
YOU IN THE BATH.

SIGNED... DATE.........

LOVE MAKES THE WORLD GO ROUND...

TO...

I PROMISE...

...TO FORGIVE YOU
AFTER AN ARGUMENT,
NO QUESTIONS ASKED.

SIGNED... DATE.....................

LOVE MAKES THE WORLD GO ROUND...